.CLASSICS.
Illustrated ®

Mark Twain
PUDD'NHEAD WILSON

essay by
Andrew J. Hoffman, Ph.D.
Brown University

ACCLAIM BOOKS

STUDY GUIDE

Pudd'nhead Wilson

art by Henry Kiefer
cover by Clem Robins

For Classics Illustrated Study Guides
computer recoloring by VanHook Studios
editor: Madeleine Robins
assistant editor: Gregg Sanderson
design: Scott Friedlander

Dale-Chall R.L.: 7.25

ISBN 1-57840-065-1

Acclaim Books, New York, NY
Printed in the United States

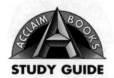

STUDY GUIDE

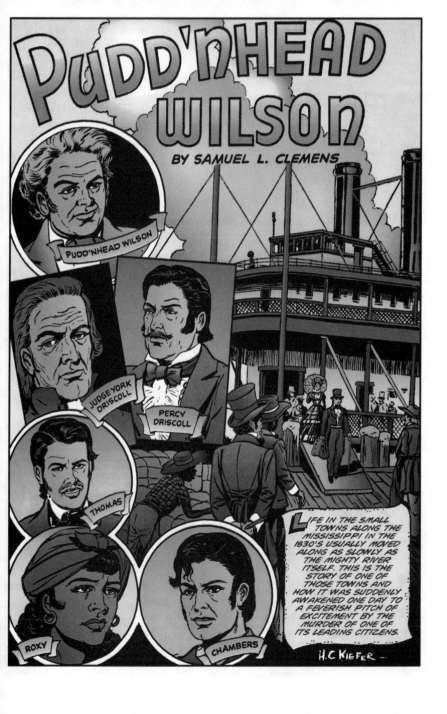

PUDD'NHEAD WILSON

BY SAMUEL L. CLEMENS

PUDD'NHEAD WILSON

JUDGE YORK DRISCOLL

PERCY DRISCOLL

THOMAS

ROXY

CHAMBERS

LIFE IN THE SMALL TOWNS ALONG THE MISSISSIPPI IN THE 1830'S USUALLY MOVED ALONG AS SLOWLY AS THE MIGHTY RIVER ITSELF. THIS IS THE STORY OF ONE OF THOSE TOWNS AND HOW IT WAS SUDDENLY AWAKENED ONE DAY TO A FEVERISH PITCH OF EXCITEMENT BY THE MURDER OF ONE OF ITS LEADING CITIZENS.

H.C KIEFER

DAWSON'S LANDING, A SLAVE HOLDING TOWN BELOW ST. LOUIS, IN THE YEAR 1830...

YOU'RE VERY FORTUNATE, PERCY. DAWSON'S LANDING IS GROWING UP, AND YOU'RE GETTING RICH WITH YOUR LAND SPECULATIONS... AND SOON YOU'LL HAVE AN HEIR TO CARRY ON AFTER YOU.

I'M NOT SO FORTUNATE, YORK.

I'VE LOST THREE CHILDREN, AND NOW THE DOCTORS FEAR FOR MY WIFE'S LIFE WITH HER COMING CHILD.

MY YOUNG BROTHER, WE ALL PRAY FOR HER.

A WEEK LATER, TWO BABIES WERE BORN AT PERCY DRISCOLL'S HOME; ONE TO HIS WIFE...

I'VE GIVEN YOU A SON BUT I WON'T LIVE TO SEE HIM GROW.

THE OTHER TO ROXY, ONE OF HIS SLAVE GIRLS.

GIT UP, ROXY. DE MASTER SAYS YOU IS TO TEND HIS AILIN' WIFE.

SO, ROXY WAS UP THE SAME DAY, TENDING BOTH BABIES AS WELL AS MRS. DRISCOLL...

A FEW DAYS LATER, MRS. PERCY DRISCOLL DIED...

I'M LEAVING MY SON THOMAS IN YOUR CARE, ROXY. I'M TOO BUSY TO LOOK AFTER HIM.

I'LL RAISE HIM FINE, MASTER. AND HE'LL HAVE MY BOY, CHAMBERS, TO GROW UP WITH.

THE SAME MONTH, DAVID WILSON, A LAWYER FROM NEW YORK, CAME TO TOWN TO SEEK HIS FORTUNE...

GOIN' TO FIND YOUR FORTUNE IN DAWSON'S LANDING, EH, FELLER?

WELL, I---

DRAT THAT HOUND! HE'S BEEN HOWLING LIKE THAT FOR AN HOUR.

BECAUSE I WOULD KILL MY HALF.

WILSON, UNFORTUNATELY, TRIED TO BE WHIMSICAL...

I WISH I OWNED HALF OF THAT DOG.

WHY?

AIN'T THEY PRETTY AND GROWIN' FAT, ESPECIALLY YOUNG MARSE TOM? DO YOU THINK HE'S CHANGED ANY, MISTER WILSON?

NO, HE LOOKS JUST THE SAME TO ME.

ROXY WAS SAFE, WILSON DIDN'T NOTICE THE SWITCH IN BABIES.

AS TIME WENT BY, THE "NEW" TOM DRISCOLL BECAME A SPOILED CHILD...

OW!

HIT 'IM! LIKE IT!

SHUT UP, CHAMBERS, OR I'LL BOX YO' EARS!

AND THE "NEW" CHAMBERS BEGAN TO LEARN HIS PLACE...

DON'T DO THAT NO MO', TOM!

DO IT ALL I WANT.

PAPA, HE'S HITTING ME!

I TOLE YOU TO STOP!

CHAMBERS SOON BECAME THE BEST FIGHTER IN TOWN...

MARSE TOM SAYS YO' IS TO LEAVE HIM ALONE!

THEY'LL BE AFRAID OF ME NOW.

...AND TOM'S BODYGUARD AND FLUNKY...

HE NEVER ONCE LET CHAMBERS USE HIS SKATES.

THAT COWARDLY DRISCOLL! I'D LIKE TO CATCH HIM ALONE!

AND TOM'S LIFE GUARD...

I CAN'T DIVE. BUT I'LL TEACH HIM A LESSON FOR SHOWING OFF IN FRONT OF THOSE WHITE BOYS.

AS CHAMBERS STARTED ANOTHER BACK SOMERSAULT, TOM GRABBED THE OARS...

...AND PULLED THE BOAT FORWARD.

WHAT A DIRTY TRICK!

NOW'S OUR CHANCE TO GET DRISCOLL!

CHAMBERS! HELP ME!

YOU KNOCKED HIM COLD! HE CAN'T HELP YOU.

CHAMBERS! CHAMBERS!

WAIT 'TIL WE GET YOU ON SHORE!

SAVE SOME FOR ME.

DRISCOLL, I'VE OWED YOU THIS FOR A LONG TIME.

THE BOYS THEN WENT TO SEE IF CHAMBERS WAS ALL RIGHT...

YOU ALL RIGHT, CHAMBERS?

YES, SUH, BUT I SHO' FEEL SHAKY. WHERE'S MARSE TOM?

DEY SAY TOM'S LYING ON SHORE, SO I GUESS I CAN REST HERE A LITTLE BIT.

LATER...

I'S SORRY, MARSE TOM. I BANGED MY HEAD. DEY WOULDN'T HAVE BEAT YOU SO IF I WAS HERE.

SHUT UP AND TAKE ME HOME.

OH, MY FACE. I'LL GET EVEN! YOU'LL BEAT THEM UP!

YES, SUH, MARSE TOM!

ONE DAY, WHEN THE TWO BOYS WERE ABOUT FIFTEEN YEARS OLD, THEY WERE OUT FOR A DAY OF SWIMMING...

WHILE OUT ALONE, TOM WAS SUDDENLY SEIZED BY A CRAMP...

HELP! I'M DROWNING!

THAT'S AN OLD TRICK! HE MAKES BELIEVE HE'S DROWNING, YOU SWIM OUT TO HIM, HE LAUGHS AT YOU, AND SWIMS AWAY. STAY HERE, CHAMBERS.

BUT TOM REALLY WAS DROWNING...

HE AIN'T NEVER TRIED DAT TRICK! I BETTER GO AFTER HIM.

AS TOM WENT DOWN FOR THE THIRD TIME...

I CAN FEEL BOTTOM NOW. I CAN TELL THE BOYS I WAS FOOLING ABOUT DROWNING. I CAN'T STAND THEM TO BELIEVE CHAMBERS RESCUED ME.

HAW! HAW! THAT BLOCK-HEAD THOUGHT I WAS REALLY DROWNING.

YOU'RE A LIAR. YOU WERE DROWNING.

HE SAVED YOUR LIFE, YOU COWARD.

I'VE WARNED YOU, WENCH, TO KEEP YOUR PLACE.

SHAME ON 'IM, HITTIN' DE MAMMY WHAT BRUNG 'IM UP.

DAT BOY AIN'T NO GOOD, NO HOW.

HE STRUCK ME, AND I WARN'T TO BLAME-- STRUCK ME IN DE FACE RIGHT BEFORE FOLKS.

OH, LORD, I DONE SO MUCH FOR HIM. I DONE LIFT HIM WAY UP TO WHAT HE IS--AND DIS IS WHAT I, GET.

LATER THAT YEAR, PERCY DRISCOLL, WORN OUT FROM TRYING TO SAVE HIS LAND SPECULATIONS AND FORTUNE, WAS ON HIS DEATH BED.

SEND FOR MY BROTHER, ROXY.

THOMAS HAS BEEN A DISAPPOINTMENT, BUT I WANT YOU TO PROMISE TO TAKE CARE OF HIM WHEN I'M DEAD.

I PROMISE.

I'M SETTING ROXY FREE. SHE'S BEEN A GOOD SLAVE AND TRIED HER BEST TO RAISE TOM PROPERLY.

ANOTHER THING, PERCY. I WANT TO BUY YOUR SLAVE, CHAMBERS. I HEAR TOM IS TRYING TO GET YOU TO SELL HIM DOWN THE RIVER. REMEMBER, HE SAVED TOM'S LIFE.

HE'S YOURS.

A MOMENT LATER, PERCY DRISCOLL WAS DEAD...

PERCY DRISCOLL'S INVESTMENTS HAD GONE BAD AND TOM WAS LEFT A PAUPER...

YOUR FATHER LOST HIS MONEY IN THE BUSTED LAND BOOM, BUT MY FORTUNE IS YOURS WHEN I'M DEAD.

THANK YOU, UNCLE.

ROXY WAS FREE...

I'S FREE, BUT I GOT NOTHIN' TO KEEP ME IN DIS TOWN. I'S GWINE TO GET A CHAMBERMAID'S JOB ON ONE OF DEM BIG MISSISSIPPI STEAM-BOATS.

AND PERCY'S OWN, REAL SON WAS LEFT A SLAVE...

ROXY DONE LEFT TO SEE DE WORLD. WISH I WAS FREE TO GO WIT HER.

Tom became completely spoiled by Judge Driscoll and his wife, who, never having had a child of their own, gave Tom everything he wanted...

THAT WOULD MAKE A FINE SADDLE HORSE.

WHY DON'T WE BUY IT FOR TOM?

ALL RIGHT.

Several years later, the judge's wife died, and at nineteen, Tom was sent to an Eastern college. There, he learned to gamble...

WHAT LUCK! I'LL HAVE TO WRITE THE JUDGE FOR MORE MONEY.

...AND DRINK.

I JUST CAN'T GRASP MY LESSONS. MAYBE THIS WHISKEY WILL CLEAR MY POOR HEAD.

After two years, Tom gave up trying to acquire an education and came home...

HOPE THE JUDGE ISN'T MAD.

Given a fine welcome home, Tom returned to his easy ways.

THAT'S ALL FOR TONIGHT, SIR.

THAT SAME YEAR, ROXY RETURNED TO DAWSON'S LANDING...

I SAVED $400 IN DE EIGHT YEARS I WORKED ON DIS BOAT. BUT DE BANK IS BUSTED AND I IS BROKE. NOW MY RHEUMATISM WON'T LET ME WORK NO MO'.

TOM DRISCOLL, WHO IS MY OWN CHAMBERS...HE WON'T FORGIT ME. HE'LL TAKE CARE OF PO' ROXY NOW.

MEANWHILE, ONE OF THE TOWNS-PEOPLE, THE WIDOW COOPER, FINALLY RENTED THE ROOM IN HER BOARDING HOUSE THAT HAD BEEN VACANT FOR MORE THAN A YEAR...

IT SAYS THERE'S TWO OF THEM. THEY'RE ITALIAN TWINS. THEY'LL BE HERE THURSDAY, ROWENA.

OH, MA, HOW ROMANTIC! JUST THINK-- ITALIAN TWINS!

THE ARRIVAL OF STRANGERS ALWAYS CAUSED EXCITEMENT IN THE SMALL TOWN...

THEIR NAMES ARE LUIGI AND ANGELO CAMPELLO. THEY'LL BE HERE THURSDAY.

MY, DON'T THEIR NAMES SOUND GRAND?

CAME THURSDAY, AND EVERYONE WAS DOWN AT THE LANDING TO MEET THE BOAT.

AND SO THE CAPELLO TWINS ARRIVED AT DAWSON'S LANDING...

THE NEXT DAY, THE ITALIAN TWINS WERE OFFICIALLY GREETED AND ACCEPTED BY THE CITIZENS...

JUDGE AND MISS DRISCOLL--COUNT ANGELO CAPELLO.

GLAD TO KNOW YOU, COUNT.

DELIGHTED, YOUR HONOR.

THE TWINS ASTOUNDED THE AUDIENCE WITH THEIR REMARKABLE PIANO PLAYING...

THE FINEST PLAYING I'VE EVER HEARD.

WONDERFUL!

WHILE ALL THE LEADING PEOPLE WERE ATTENDING THE TWINS' WELCOME, TOM, IN DISGUISE, ROBBED THEIR HOMES...

AH, A GOLD WATCH!

AND LATER ATTENDED THE PARTY, WHERE HE ROBBED THE TWINS OF A BEJEWELED KNIFE...

HERE'S MY CHANCE TO GO UP-STAIRS AND SEE WHAT I CAN GET FROM THE ITALIANS...

THE NEXT DAY, THE TWINS AND TOM VISITED PUDD'NHEAD WILSON...

I DON'T KNOW WHY PUDD'NHEAD WANTS MY PRINTS AGAIN. HE'S GOT SO MANY SETS OF THEM ALREADY.

NEXT, HAVING HEARD THAT PUDD'NHEAD WILSON READ PALMS, LUIGI ASKED THAT HIS BE READ...

GO AHEAD, DON'T BE AFRAID TO SAY WHAT YOU SEE THERE.

WELL, YOU ASKED FOR IT.

YOU HAVE KILLED SOMEONE, BUT WHETHER MAN, WOMAN OR CHILD, I CANNOT MAKE OUT.

CAESAR'S GHOST! WHAT DID YOU LET HIM READ IT FOR?

HE KILLED A MAN TO SAVE MY LIFE. I'LL EXPLAIN.

"THE GAIKOWAR OF BARODA GAVE LUIGI A BEAUTIFUL KNIFE IN A JEWELED SHEATH. THE KNIFE WAS WORTH A FORTUNE, AND HAD BEEN IN THE GAIKOWAR'S FAMILY FOR CENTURIES..."

IF YOU MUST EVER USE IT, STRIKE DOWN!

"THAT NIGHT, I WAS ASLEEP, BUT LUIGI, AWAKE, THOUGHT HE HEARD A NOISE..."

"LUIGI GRABBED THE WOULD-BE ASSASSIN'S WRIST AND..."

I HOPE YOU TWO ARE NOT HARMED

WE ARE ALL RIGHT, YOUR HIGHNESS.

LUIGI STILL HAS THAT KNIFE.

IT'S A GOOD THING I CAME. I THOUGHT THE JEWELS WERE GLASS, AND I WOULD HAVE SOLD THAT KNIFE FOR A SONG.

SOMETIME LATER, THE TWINS WERE INVITED TO A POLITICAL RALLY...

VOTE for WILSON

THE NEXT DAY, TOM HAD LUIGI ARRESTED, AND, AFTER WAITING TWENTY YEARS, PUDD'NHEAD WILSON GOT HIS FIRST CASE...

IN SPITE OF YOUR EXCELLENT PRESENTATION OF THE CASE, MR. WILSON, I FIND THE DEFENDANT GUILTY, BUT FINE HIM ONLY FIVE DOLLARS. THAT OUGHT TO SATISFY EVERYBODY.

JUDGE DRISCOLL, RETURNING FROM A FISHING TRIP, LEARNED OF TOM'S DISGRACE...

YOU SHOULD HAVE CHALLENGED HIM TO A DUEL AS ANY SOUTHERN GENTLEMAN WOULD.

I'M AFRAID OF THE MURDEROUS DEVIL. DON'T MAKE ME FIGHT HIM!

I NEVER BELIEVED A DRISCOLL COULD BE A COWARD. I'M DESTROYING THIS WILL AND DISOWNING YOU! GET OUT!

FOR MY DEAD BROTHER'S HONOR, I'LL FIGHT THE DUEL MYSELF. MY GOOD FRIEND, HOWARD, WILL BE MY SECOND.

LUIGI ACCEPTED THE JUDGE'S CHALLENGE AND THE JUDGE PUT HIS AFFAIRS IN GOOD ORDER IN THE EVENT HE WAS KILLED...

MAYBE I'LL BE KILLED. HE'S STILL PERCY'S SON AND ENTITLED TO MY FORTUNE. I'LL WRITE A NEW WILL.

HE'S WRITING A NEW WILL. I MUST STOP MY GAMBLING AND PAY MY DEBTS, AND GET BACK IN HIS GOOD GRACES.

FORTUNATELY FOR HER, ROXY FOUND A CANOE AT THE RIVER'S EDGE...

DE LORD BE PRAISED. DAT'S THE GRAND MOGUL, MY OLD BOAT. I'S SAVED.

ROXY WAS ONCE AGAIN AMONG FRIENDS...

I'S A FREE WOMAN, BUT I WAS SOLD A SLAVE DOWN THE RIVER.

WE'LL GET YOU BACK TO DAWSON'S LANDING, ROXY.

ROXY LEARNED THAT TOM WAS IN ST. LOUIS AND WHEN THE BOAT STOPPED THERE, SHE FOUND HIM...

I DON'T TRUST YOU AN' I'S A KNIFE IN MY POCKET. AN' I KIN —— USE IT.

I THOUGHT I WAS DOING WHAT WAS BEST FOR YOU, MA.

SELL YO' OWN MOTHER DOWN DE RIVER. YOU IS DE LOWEST DOG THAT WAS EVER PUP'D.

WHAT CAN I DO, MA?

YOU IS GWINE TO TAKE ALL YO' MONEY AN' GET DE REST FROM DE JUDGE AN' YOU IS GWINE TO BUY ME FREE.

THE JUDGE WILL NEVER GIVE ME THE MONEY. I'LL HAVE TO STEAL IT FROM HIM.

IN A MATTER OF MOMENTS, THE ROOM WAS CROWDED WITH NEIGHBORS...

SAY, AIN'T THAT THE KNIFE THEM ITALIANS CLAIMED THEY LOST?

REMEMBER THE JUDGE SAID THEY'D FIND IT WHEN THEY NEEDED TO ASSAS-SINATE SOMEBODY?

MAYOR PUDD'NHEAD WILSON QUICKLY TOOK COMMAND...

I SEE THERE IS NO BLOOD ON YOUR HANDS, BUT THERE IS ON THE KNIFE AND HANDLE.

LUIGI WAS ARRESTED FOR MURDER, AND ANGELO AS AN ACCESSORY...

WILSON, MEANWHILE, EXAMINED THE FINGER-PRINTS ON THE KNIFE HANDLE...

THE FINGER-PRINTS ON THE KNIFE DEFINITELY DO NOT BELONG TO EITHER OF THE TWINS. BUT WHOSE CAN THEY BE?

BECAUSE THE CLARKSON GIRLS SAID THEY SAW A WOMAN RUNNING OUT OF THE JUDGE'S HOUSE, WILSON COMPARED ALL OF THE FEMALE SETS OF PRINTS HE HAD WITH THAT ON THE HANDLE, BUT COULD NOT FIND A MATCHING SET.

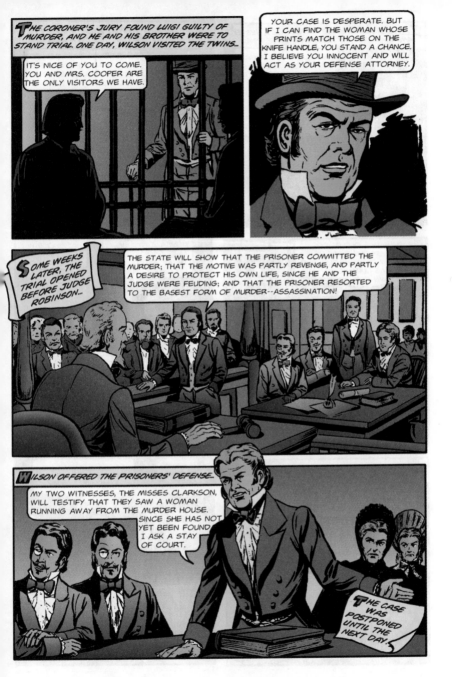

TOM HAD TAKEN OVER THE JUDGE'S MONEY, AND HAD BOUGHT ROXY HER FREEDOM...

USUALLY, IN A MURDER, THE MURDERER LEAVES SOME CLUE. BUT MINE IS A PERFECT CASE. WILSON IS LOOKING FOR A WOMAN WHO DOESN'T EXIST, AND I, AS EVERYONE KNOWS, WAS IN ST. LOUIS AT THAT TIME. HA!

TOM DECIDED TO VISIT PUDD'NHEAD THAT NIGHT TO BOLSTER HIS OWN MORALE...

SO YOU'VE GONE BACK TO YOUR CHILDISH HOBBY FOR CONSOLATION. CHEER UP, YOU'LL LOSE THE CASE, BUT YOU'LL BE ALL RIGHT.

WHY HERE'S OLD ROXY'S LABEL. BY THE DATE HERE, I WAS 7 MONTHS OLD, AND SHE WAS NURSING ME AND HER OWN CUB.

THAT'S A STRAIGHT LINE ACROSS HER THUMB-PRINT. HOW COMES THAT?

THAT IS COMMON. SCAR OF A CUT OR SCRATCH.

BUT AS WILSON HELD ROXY'S SLIDE TO THE LIGHT...

WHAT'S THE MATTER, PUDD'NHEAD? YOU'RE AS WHITE AS A SHEET.

JUST OVERTIRED. YOU BETTER LEAVE, DRISCOLL.

AS SOON AS TOM LEFT...

I FEEL SORRY FOR HIM, EVEN THOUGH HE IS A MISERABLE DOG.

PUDD'NHEAD GOT A LAUGH THE NEXT MORNING WHEN HE BROUGHT SOME OF HIS SLIDES OF FINGER-PRINTS INTO COURT...

THIS NEW EVIDENCE, DEALING WITH FINGER-PRINTS, CAME TO ME LAST NIGHT, AND I AM SUBMITTING IT AS EVIDENCE NOW.

HA! OUR MAYOR IS STILL A PUDD'NHEAD!

WHAT A LAWYER!

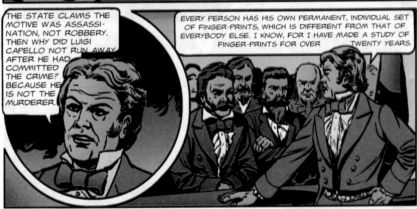

THE STATE CLAIMS THE MOTIVE WAS ASSASSINATION, NOT ROBBERY. THEN WHY DID LUIGI CAPELLO NOT RUN AWAY AFTER HE HAD COMMITTED THE CRIME? BECAUSE HE IS NOT THE MURDERER.

EVERY PERSON HAS HIS OWN PERMANENT, INDIVIDUAL SET OF FINGER-PRINTS, WHICH IS DIFFERENT FROM THAT OF EVERYBODY ELSE. I KNOW, FOR I HAVE MADE A STUDY OF FINGER-PRINTS FOR OVER TWENTY YEARS.

WILSON TURNED HIS BACK AND ASKED FOR VOLUNTEERS TO RUB THEIR HANDS THROUGH THEIR HAIR, AND THEN GO OVER AND LEAVE THEIR PRINTS ON A WINDOW...

THESE ARE JUDGE ROBINSON'S PRINTS. HERE ARE THE SHERIFF'S. THESE ARE MR. HOWARD'S. HERE ARE MRS. PRATT'S. HERE'S LUIGI'S AND HERE, ANGELO'S.

PUDD'NHEAD WILSON
MARK TWAIN

Mark Twain's later work—the books and essays written after his publishing firm went bankrupt in 1893—has always struggled for both readers and respect. Composed just as his world crashed around him, *Pudd'nhead Wilson* has achieved the most success among his novels from this period. Especially over the past two decades, this story of murder, betrayal and obscured identity has surged to the forefront of Twain's work. Fueled by its blunt and brutal assessment of the role of race in America's slave-holding South—and by implication the role of race in America since slavery was abolished—*Pudd'nhead Wilson* has become one of the most passionately debated works in American literature. The absence of a hero on a grand traditional scale, combined with the long-delayed success of the title character, David Wilson, give the novel a deeply modern feel, as though Mark Twain had seen into the heart of 20th century anxiety over identity and the individual's relationship with his or her society. Roxy, the slave woman who switches her son with her master's in order to save him, finds out what can happen to someone who dares to break the social code on race; her son's punishment for committing murder almost pales in comparison. *Pudd'nhead Wilson*'s "moral astringency," as a leading critic once called it, makes the novel as bright, powerful and important today as when it was first published over and century ago.

The Author

When Samuel Langhorne Clemens was born in Missouri in 1835, slavery was a fundamental part of his world. His family owned one slave, Jennie, who helped rear all seven Clemens children; young Sam once saw his father whip Jennie with a bridle for threatening Sam's mother. The family's move to the larger and more commercial river town of Hannibal, when Clemens was just four, brought him in closer contact with the rule of the lash. Missouri was a prime battleground for the growing conflict over the issue of slavery, and slave-traders, bounty hunters, and abolitionists all crowded the shores of the Mississippi river. Sam's father earned some badly-needed community respect once for when he sat on a jury which imposed a harsh sentence on Northern abolitionists who had helped some local slaves to freedom.

After his father's death, when he was eleven, Sam entered the newspaper business, mostly working with his older brother Orion. He later capitalized on a chance to join in the Mississippi River trade as steamboat pilot, his childhood ambition (the Classics Illustrated edition appears to show Twain helping Roxy aboard a steamboat). When the inevitable Civil War came, it put a stop to Clemens's successful four-year run on the river; the war between the North and South ended most travel along the river. After a brief and unsuccessful stint in a tiny Confederate military troop made up of his childhood friends from Hannibal, Clemens sat out the remainder of the conflict by heading west to Nevada with his brother, whom President Abraham Lincoln had appointed Secretary of the new territory. After prospecting half-heartedly for a few months, Sam landed a job at the West's finest newspaper, and began signing the name Mark Twain to his journalism in the Virginia City, Nevada *Territorial Enterprise*, in February

of 1863. Within five years, Mark Twain had become the nation's most popular writer and comedian.

Mark Twain's first two books of personal adventure—*Innocents Abroad*, about his trip to Europe and the Middle East, and *Roughing It*, about his years in the Wild West—established his name and fame. He married a wealthy woman and together with her built a magnificent mansion in Hartford, Connecticut. They had four children, one of whom died in infancy, and Sam Clemens divided his time between caring for his family, writing popular books, performing publicly as Mark Twain, and speculating in new technology in order to become wealthier. He invested heavily in a number of machines, none of which produced much income, and in 1884 established his own publishing house, Charles L. Webster and Company, named for his nephew-by-marriage, who ran it. He had begun the company because he felt his earlier publishers had robbed him of his rightful profits. As his own publisher, he could pocket both his royalty and the share due the provider of the capital.

Webster and Company had

ROXY WAS ONCE AGAIN AMONG FRIENDS...

IS A FREE WOMAN, BUT I WAS SOLD A SLAVE DOWN THE RIVER.

WE'LL GET YOU BACK TO DAWSON'S LANDING, ROXY.

two immediate successes, Mark Twain's *Adventures of Huckleberry Finn* and *The Personal Memoirs of Ulysses S. Grant*, the victorious Civil War general and immensely popular, if ineffective, president. But Clemens had misplaced his faith in his niece's husband: Charley Webster discovered that running a successful publishing company was beyond his capacity. Whether Webster succumbed to drug abuse or illness is not clear, but before he relinquished the reins of the company he committed it to sell a multi-volume encyclopedia of American literature. The excellent collection would have been profitable in the long run, if Clemens had enough money to keep it afloat long enough, but he had instead invested almost $200,000 in a mechanical typesetter. Both the typesetter and the publishing company went belly up, and by the early 1890s Clemens was deeply in debt. He closed up his Hartford mansion and moved his family to Europe, where they could live more economically.

Clemens traveled back and forth from Europe to America to attend to his affairs, and during the multiple Atlantic crossings he conceived, and then reconceived, *Pudd'nhead Wilson*. It started out as a farce, with the arrival in a small Mississippi River town of Siamese twins, who claim to be Italian counts, stripped of their title and only recently escaped from virtual slavery. Perhaps it was the image of the twins, or the escape from slavery, or Clemens's imaginary return to the land of his youth, but the story began to transform itself under his very pen. Two minor characters took over the action and sent the novel spinning off in a totally unpredictable direction. It took Clemens many weird and wild revisions to separate the old farce from the new tragedy. He published *Pudd'nhead Wilson* serially, as his bankruptcy proceedings dominated his every waking moment.

In order to repay his debts, Clemens agreed to take Mark Twain on an around-the-world tour, which took him across the United States and Canada, to Australia, India and South Africa. Soon after Clemens, his wife, and their middle daughter arrived in England, they received word that Susy, the eldest child, was ill. Livy and Clara boarded a ship to race to her side, so Clemens had to read news of his daughter's death alone. The Clemens family was never the same after Susy's death: they never celebrated birthdays or holidays, Livy seldom went out, and Clemens's writing took on a desperate and difficult edge. He repaid his debts in full, however, and between 1900 and his death in 1910, Mark Twain was the most photographed and the most recognizable American in the world.

Mark Twain and Identity

Few people in history have withstood as much confusion over identity as did Samuel Langhorne Clemens. For a large portion of his life, and to most people in the world, he was simply Mark Twain, the noted writer and humorist. But Clemens himself knew that Mark Twain was an invention, the semblance of a real person but really just a persona, a fictional character. During the first decade of Mark Twain's existence, Clemens easily kept his private self and his public one separate, except when touring as Mark Twain. Then the strain of pretending to be constantly genial, endlessly wise, and insightfully funny wore him down. After one unpleasant tour, a series of illnesses at home, and a year of writing a long monthly magazine column, he exploded to his brother, "Haven't I risked cheapening myself sufficiently by a year's periodical dancing before the public but I must continue it?" He fumed, "I lay awake all last night aggravating myself with this prospect of seeing my hated nom de plume (for I do loathe the very sight of it) in print again every month." Even during the years of his greatest success, he took to signing both his names across one another, like an X, as though trying to cancel himself out.

But he couldn't shake his alternate persona. His public, primed by his frequent performances as Mark Twain, expected Clemens to *be* Mark Twain. When he stopped performing for a while, bad imitators mined the available gold to be made by playing the humorist. To protect his invention and his income, Clemens often went to court to stop any misappropriation of Mark Twain. In this way, Mark Twain was both Clemens's sources of fame and wealth, and a burden he could never shake. Though many contemporary performers—movie and rock stars, especially—suffer the same fate as Clemens had a hundred and twenty years ago, Clemens had no model to help him through this identity crisis. Never before

had a man's public self achieved so dominant a level of fame that his private self was so completely overpowered.

In *Pudd'nhead Wilson*, Clemens explored how it felt to have a public identity inescapably determined. David Wilson earns the name Pudd'nhead ten minutes into his arrival at Dawson's Landing, and cannot shake the nickname for more than twenty years. Roxy, despite her fair hair and light skin, has enough Negro blood in her to bar her forever and always from full participation in her society. Her obvious majesty, her brilliance, her great strength of character—qualities which by right ought to lead her to a position of dominance in the community, count for nothing. Her public identity is so carefully circumscribed by law and custom that her true identity—the woman she really is—have no effect. In the end, she's only her public self, tragically reduced to enduring the one fate she had hoped to escape, the sale of her son down-river.

> IN MY OPINION, HE'S A LUMMOX.

> IT AIN'T GOIN' TOO FAR TO SAY HE'S A PUDDNHEAD.

In some ways, Clemens came to terms with the inescapability of his public persona through writing *Pudd'nhead Wilson*. Roxy achieves a sort of redemption through the public recognition of her private tragedy, even though it's only understood through the collective courtroom of Dawson's Landing. As Sam Clemens entered his final decade and a half, he stopped trying to define the differences between himself and Mark Twain. On his world tour as Mark Twain, he began to accept his popular identity as a "close-enough" approximation of himself. In his last few years, when he began dictating his life story, he did so with the clear aim of reducing the distance between his two selves, altering his stories only when the distance between Mark Twain and Sam Clemens grew too wide. He recognized, in the end, that Mark Twain was his one hope for life after death. He has achieved it, perhaps more than any literary figure except William Shakespeare.

Roxy: though only one-sixteenth Negro, she's a slave woman when the book opens, free later; she is the mother of "Tom Driscoll," from an affair with a leading white citizen of Dawson's Landing.

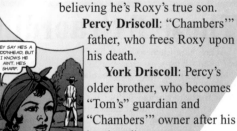

DEY SAY HE'S A PUDD'NHEAD, BUT I KNOWS HE AINT. HE'S SHARP.

David "Pudd'nhead" Wilson: a native of New York, college educated and a graduate of an Eastern law school, Wilson nonetheless cannot get a foothold in Dawson's Landing, but instead of moving on bides his time there for twenty-three years.

"Tom Driscoll:" actually Roxy's son, Valet de Chambre, after being switched in the cradle for the true heir of the Driscoll fortune, born at the same time and both under Roxy's care; "Tom" grows into a violent, ungrateful gambler.

"Chambers:" actually Thomas á Becket Driscoll, the true heir; "Chambers" grows up a slave, believing he's Roxy's true son.

Percy Driscoll: "Chambers'" father, who frees Roxy upon his death.

York Driscoll: Percy's older brother, who becomes "Tom's" guardian and "Chambers'" owner after his brother dies.

Mrs. Pratt: widowed sister of the Driscoll brothers, also guardian to "Tom."

Pembroke Howard: York Driscoll's closest friend, another member of the elite of Dawson's Landing.

Luigi and Angelo Capello: twins, ostensibly Italian counts, who have chosen to visit Dawson's Landing for uncertain reasons.

Patsy Cooper: a poor widow, landlady to the twin Italian counts.

Rowena Cooper: Patsy's daughter, foolishly fascinated by the Italians.

John Buckstone: a local politician.

Justice Robinson: the town judge, after York Driscoll's retirement.

Jim Blake: the town constable.

Dawson's Landing: in many ways, the town itself is a vital character in the novel, and the spirit of the community propels the action not only in the courtroom climax but throughout the novel.

AND CHAMBERS, THE REAL TOM DRISCOLL, WAS RESIGNED TO HIS LOT AS A SLAVE..

HURRY UP WIT DAT WOOD, YOU LAZY HEAD. I NEEDS SOME FOR DE STOVE.

"Those Extraordinary Twins"

When Sam Clemens published *Pudd'nhead Wilson* as a book in 1894, he included with it an eighty-page explanation of what he had removed from the novel to make it turn out the way it did. It's difficult to say why he included this section, called "Those Extraordinary Twins." Perhaps he felt the novel was too short to sell alone, or perhaps he thought the added material would induce people who had read the novel as a serial in *Century* magazine to buy it in book form. It's possible, too that he regarded *Pudd'nhead Wilson* as too serious a work to publish just as he was attempting to resurrect Mark Twain as a stage comedian through his world tour. Whatever reason Clemens had for publishing it, it's an extraordinary document.

"A man who is not born with the novel-writing gift has a troublesome time of it when he tries to build a novel," Mark Twain opens his essay. "I know this from experience." He explains that the forgoing novel had given him great trouble in the composition, and that he had tried many solutions to the problem. The book had started as a comic romp involving the Italian twins, but in the original they were linked at the torso and had but a single pair of legs between them. Twain wrote that he thought he could solve the problem by separating the twins, but then he had the whole set of characters around them, especially Rowena Cooper, who was cast as "an ass [who] said such stupid and irritating things and was so nauseatingly sentimental." He decides to simply drown her in the well. It seemed such a simple and elegant solution, "I hunted up the two boys and said 'they went out back one night to stone the cat and fell down the well and got drowned.' Next I search around and found out old Aunt Patsy Cooper and Aunt Betsy Hale where they were aground, and said 'they went out back one night to visit the sick and fell down the well and got drowned.' I was going to drown some of the others, but I gave up the idea," Twain noted, "partly because it was not a large

well and would not hold any more." Eventually he settled on a better solution: he removed the farce—"a kind of literary Caesarean operation"—and left behind the tragedy.

But "Those Extraordinary Twins" is not just a silly empty comedy. It contains evidence that Clemens had an even more daring literary imagination than that great one with which he's normally credited. There are many good reasons for having kept the twins linked, not the least of which would be to demonstrate how the two aspects of society in Dawson's Landing, slave and free, are inextricably interdependent. But the absurd twins would have been a powerful surrealistic gesture from a writer best known for his realism. In fact, Mark Twain's imagination had always tended toward the surreal, a tendency he subverted into comedy. But surrealism in literature was still many decades away, and Sam Clemens, desperate for a successful book to help him solve his financial problems, couldn't afford to place *Pudd'nhead Wilson* on the advance front of artistic invention.

THE ARRIVAL OF STRANGERS ALWAYS CAUSED EXCITEMENT IN THE SMALL TOWN...

THEIR NAMES ARE LUIGI AND ANGELO CAMPELLO. THEY'LL BE HERE THURSDAY.

MY, DON'T THEIR NAMES SOUND GRAND?

Still, Clemens could not entirely let go of his surreal farce. He not only included it in the book version of the novel; he also left many vestiges of it in the novel itself. For example, when Angelo begins telling the twin's history he says, "Our parents were well to do, there in Italy, and we were their only child." And at a drunken political meeting, Tom refers to the twins as a "human philopena," a fancy word for a pair of scissors, an apt description of two men with but a single set of legs between them, but not of twins. The remains imply that Clemens, normally an immensely careful craftsman, intended to leave a shadow of the former story. This implied desire has made it very difficult to publish a critical edition of *Pudd'nhead Wilson*. Should it include "Those Extraordinary Twins" or not? Should the surreal elements of the farce be returned to the tragedy? No one has yet answered these questions.

In *Pudd'nhead Wilson*, Mark Twain makes inventive use of a very old plot device, the switch story, in which people of opposite positions in society trade places, usually with comic results. More than a decade before publishing this novel, Twain himself took advantage of the comic possibilities of switched identities in another novel, *The Prince and the Pauper*. But while he embedded a gentle political critique in the earlier book, *Pudd'nhead Wilson* pulls no punches in order to make a joke or teach a history lesson. He uses the confusion of identities to ask some challenging questions: What is the nature of human identity? What effect does an individual's identity have with his or her role in society? How much of one's behavior can be traced to in-born traits? What is the role of justice in a society where these other questions of identity remain unanswered? And what do we mean by success in an unjust society?

The action in *Pudd'nhead Wilson* all stems from Roxy rashly switching the six-month-old infants in her care. At this age, Tom and Chambers look astonishingly alike; the way Twain later describes the literal twins, Angelo and Luigi Capello, described the small boys: "One was a little fairer than the other, but otherwise they were exact duplicates." Desperate after watching all the other slaves owned by Percy Driscoll sold for stealing, Roxy at first determines to kill herself and her son. Seeing her son dressed in Tom's finery gives Roxy the idea to switch the boys. Within a few short years, likeness between the boys dissolves. "'Tom' got all the petting, 'Chambers' got none. 'Tom' got all the delicacies, 'Chambers' got mush and milk, and clabber without sugar. In consequence 'Tom' was a sickly child and 'Chambers' wasn't. 'Tom' was 'fractious,' as Roxy called it, and overbearing; 'Chambers' was meek and docile."

But the physical and psychological differences between the boys amounts to little when compared with their social differences: the new Chambers becomes Tom's proxy in fighting, stealing and other deviltry, but he never receives any benefit from his actions, and is beaten without mercy if he resents the inequitable distribution of rewards. (See panel on next page). (The Classics Illustrated adaptation overestimates the importance of Tom's brutality to Chambers. It spends almost 20% of the comic demonstrating their boyhood rela-

SHE PUT ONE OF TOM'S SUITS ON CHAMBERS.

YOU IS JIST AS PRETTY AS MARSE TOM WHY YESTERDAY, YOU WAS BOTH IN DE TUB, AND MASTER PERCY HAD TO ASK ME WHICH ONE WAS HIS.

LET ME GO! I'LL KILL HIM!

RUN HOME, CHAMBERS, YOUR MAMMY WILL BANDAGE YOU.

FORTUNATELY, CHAMBERS WAS NOT SERIOUSLY WOUNDED. SUCH WAS TOM DRISCOLL'S CHARACTER. BUT HAD HIS MOTHER PROFITED BY CHANGING HIM FROM A SLAVE TO A MASTER.

tionship; Twain wrote barely two pages out of nearly two hundred to cover the same material.) This social disparity is important because it is embodied in Tom Driscoll, who lives a life of white privilege but fears he will fall into the netherworld of slavery at any moment. He flunks out of Yale and returns to Dawson's Landing with the habits of a gentleman, including excessive drinking and gambling. Though he flirts with disaster, he makes no secret of his sole ambition: to inherit his uncle's wealth—and position in society.

By the time Tom returns from college, David Wilson has been in Dawson's Landing for 20 years. Despite his excellent credentials, Wilson has never received the honor of a legal case. His off-hand joke about a distant barking dog—"I wish I owned half that dog." "Why?" somebody asked. "Because I would kill my half."—brands him as a fool. Though "in time he came to be liked, and well liked, too, . . . that first day's verdict made him a fool, and he was not able to get it set aside, or even modified." He makes his money with a little surveying and book-

keeping, bides his time with the study of finger-prints, and amuses himself by composing epigrams. Only Judge York Driscoll, Tom's long-suffering uncle, and Roxy, Tom's natural mother, know Wilson's true worth. After Roxy switches the infants, she worries one man will discover her secret. "Dey calls him a pudd'nhead, en says he's a fool. My lan', dat man ain't no mo' fool den I is! He's the smartes' man in dis town." Plot balance requires that Roxy and Wilson eventually square off.

Following Tom's return from college, the action of the novel shifts away from Roxy's heroic but ill-considered choice and toward the conflict buried in Tom Driscoll. He finds he must keep his true self a secret from society. At first he believes the secret is his addiction to gambling, but the reappearance of Roxy and, with her, the truth of his birth, gives him a great secret to guard. The truth is that he's "a slave and, by a fiction of law and custom, a negro." The 1/32nd part of his heritage outvotes the majority, and thus makes his life a sham. Of course, Tom is ready to believe this because his life has always been a sham. He not only hides his gambling debts, he dresses in women's clothes to rob his neighbors in order to pay those debts.

The appearance of Luigi and Angelo Capello drives the last half of the book. They rapidly become all that Tom himself cannot, despite his education, breeding and superficial nicety. They are popular around town and so quickly embraced by the community that they are nominated for public office. When Pudd'nhead Wilson's palm-reading reveals the murderous secret of the bejeweled knife Tom has stolen from the twins, Tom is not repulsed but rather overwhelmed by the shabbiness of his own secret

as compared with the Capello's. Tom conceives a hatred for the twins only when they publicly humiliate him for the insult he has launched out of jealousy.

Desperate to eliminate all his problems at once, Tom accepts Roxy's offer that Tom sell her back into slavery in order to repay his debts, and then traitorously sells his own mother down-river, to the cotton plantations which consumed slaves as if they were fuel. His perfidy has not taken Roxy's great courage into account, however. She breaks free and returns to find her wretched son. At last driven to the limit of his skill and patience, Tom robs his own uncle. When York Driscoll wakes to find a woman, Tom in disguise, rooting after his money, Tom stabs him with the knife he has stolen from the Italian twins. The twins, out for a walk, hear the Judge's screams and enter the front door while Tom escapes out the back. Discovered there and arrested, the twins give Pudd'nhead Wilson his first serious legal case.

To the casual onlooker, the twins' case is hopeless. Luigi and the Judge had recently conducted a duel, which York Driscoll had initiated to defend the humiliated honor of his cowardly nephew. Then, during the political campaign, the Judge had leveled a damning comment at Luigi—that he would find his lost knife "whenever he should have the occasion *to assassinate somebody*"—which cost the Italians the election. Finally, the judge refused to meet a murderer for another duel, which meant the two men were expected to shoot one another on sight. In the view of most people in

Dawson's Landing, Luigi Capello had gotten the drop on the old Judge, and now he has to face the law. Tom Driscoll feels entirely secure in the belief that he had committed the perfect crime. "There's not even the faintest suggestion of a trace [of evidence] left. No more than a bird leaves when it flies through the air—yes, through the night, you may say. The man that can track a bird through the air in the dark and find that bird is the man to track me out."

Of course, Pudd'nhead Wilson is that man. The assassin has left his finger-prints on ivory handle of Luigi's valuable knife. It thus takes Wilson no time at all to satisfy himself that the prints don't match either of the Italians, but he knows that, unless he can provide the person whose prints *do* match, the jury will convict the twins out of a primitive need for

WILSON, MEANWHILE, EXAMINED THE FINGER-PRINTS ON THE KNIFE HANDLE.

THE FINGER-PRINTS ON THE KNIFE DEFINITELY DO NOT BELONG TO EITHER OF THE TWINS. BUT WHOSE CAN THEY BE?

B ECAUSE THE CLARKSON GIRLS SAID THEY SAW A WOMAN RUNNING OUT OF THE JUDGE'S HOUSE, WILSON COMPARED ALL OF THE FEMALE SETS OF PRINTS HE HAD WITH THAT ON THE HANDLE. BUT COULD NOT FIND A MATCHING SET.

Finger Printing and Identity

Many contemporary readers forget that knowledge of the differences in finger-prints is relatively new. Today, children are routinely finger printed to protect them. Criminals are always finger printed, and those prints are now compared through computer with the thousands of prints of known criminals currently on file with police departments. Soon, credit cards will have computerized finger-print identification systems built right into them. A century ago, however, finger-prints were as novel as DNA typing is today. The courtroom confusion over DNA technology is nothing compared with the legal confusion

over finger-prints then. Remember that today many people refer to genetic typing as "DNA finger printing." DNA is now just another version of the most basic tool we have for determining a person's identity.

The role of finger-printing in identification, as pioneered by Sir Francis Galton in his 1892 book *Finger Prints*, required a vast mental adjustment. Prior to that time, individuality was seen as a somewhat muted thing, a romantic concept of importance to firebrands but of no use to the smooth operation of society. People were more typically spoken of in classes or families, and the role of the psyche

NOW, ROXY, RUB YOUR FINGERS THROUGH YOUR HAIR. THE NATURAL OIL WILL ENABLE ME TO GET YOUR FINGER-PRINTS!

WHAT FOR YOU WANT DE FINGER-PRINTS OF A POOR SLAVE LIKE ME?

JUST A HOBBY. I WANT TO COLLECT THE PRINTS OF EVERYONE IN TOWN.

justice. Tom comes to tease Wilson the night before his closing arguments, when the case looks the bleakest, and accidentally leaves the finger-prints that will convict him. The following morning, Wilson leads the court through the details and the meaning of what has appeared to the town of Dawson's Landing to be the lifelong occupation of a fool, the study of the small lines on the skin of people's fingertips. To Wilson—and to us, now that we recognize the individuality of fingerprints—these lines are the unfalsifiable autograph of one's identity, and he uses them to prove not only the innocence of the twins, and not only the guilt of Tom Driscoll, but also the truth of Tom's birth identity.

This fact is entirely irrelevant to the exoneration of his clients and the resolution of the murder. Why does Pudd'nhead Wilson insist on making this point in open court? The simplest answer is that truth and justice require it. The true Tom Driscoll has been deprived of his freedom and his fortune for more than twenty years, and it must be restored to him. In fact, that answer is more complex. The integrity of Dawson's Landing,

as an aspect of individuation was under vehement discussion. The sense that a person had an identity—that is, an essential and individual character belonging only to him or her—was a revolutionary idea, literally. How can one maintain that differences in sex, race or ethnic origin count for very much when it's manifestly clear that the differences between *people within a group* are much greater than the differences *between groups*? In many ways this very concept of human individuality has led to the most progressive changes in society over the past century.

But identity is not simply a way to distinguish one person from another. Even the most adamant individualists will agree that society, and social roles, determine a great deal about how one behaves. In fact, most people would agree that only a tiny part of behavior can be traced to some ineffable and essential identity buried deeply below surface conventions. Even appearance, the most obvious tool of individuation, is subject to radical change. What is a make-over but the alteration of a person's appearance to bring him or her closer to a social norm of beauty?

Mark Twain was aware of these troubling aspects of identity, as he signals at the beginning of *Pudd'nhead Wilson*. When Wilson makes his joke about the dog his first day in Dawson's Landing, the first comment is, "'Pears to be a fool." To which another man replies, "'Pears? *Is*, I reckon you better say." The people of Dawson's Landing are completely unaware of any great distance between the public and the essential self, between appearance and reality. But Wilson, because he is a student of it, and Tom Driscoll, because he is a practitioner of it, know that social dissembling is the rule. Wilson believes that there is an essential person behind the mask; Driscoll merely believes in the mask and fears the person behind it. In *Pudd'nhead Wilson*, however, identity is not a tool for the radical *remaking* of society, but rather the tool for *restoring* its fundamental prejudice and injustice. It is an open question whether Mark Twain himself was aware of this irony.

such as it is, has been compromised by the presence of a slave in a position of power, and only by restoring the social order can the community be redeemed. As narrative symmetry requires, Wilson has confronted Roxy's heroic deception and bound her son to the very fate she had hoped the switch would save him from. "Everybody granted that if 'Tom' were white and free it would be unquestionably right to punish him," Twain concludes. "But to shut up a valuable slave for life—that was quite another matter. As soon as the Governor understood the case, he pardoned Tom at once, and the creditors sold him down the river." Wilson has also secured himself the position of leadership in Dawson's Landing; "he was a made man for good." But even the town acknowledges that though David Wilson is no longer a pudd'nhead, every member of the town is. By restoring to Dawson's Landing its fundamental level of injustice, Wilson has merely become the first citizen of a community of idiots.

Themes

Perhaps the single most remarkable aspect of *Pudd'nhead Wilson* is its rigorous moral vision. We have no trouble determining that Tom Driscoll is a bad man, of course; Mark Twain would have strained belief if he made him any worse than he already is. But guaging the relative virtue of the other players in the drama is more difficult. And yet, weighing the moral value of the novel's characters provides the quickest in-road into understanding the themes of the book. In *Pudd'nhead Wilson*, characters have moral positions attached to them, and their conduct and rationales tell us which positions to value.

Dawson's Landing

As noted above, the town is very much a character in this drama, much as the chorus in ancient Greek drama personifies the community. Twain portrays the town as idyllic, "a snug little collection of one- and two-storey frame dwellings whose white-washed exteriors were almost concealed from sight by climbing tangles of rose-vines, honeysuckles, and morning-glories." Geography itself isolates the town, bordered as it is by the river and the hills, which "rose high, inclosing the town in a half-moon curve." Nearly all the action in the novel takes place within this perfect little community; only Tom, the town's source of immorality can break the boundaries. Even David Wilson, once he arrives in Dawson's Landing, cannot leave.

But Twain's description of the town reveals his intention. Beautiful flowers almost conceal the lily-white facades of the houses, but not quite. The houses look pretty, seem to embody a moral rectitude, but they don't. Twain tells us what lies behind these fine homes. "Dawson's Landing was a slave-holding town, with rich slave-worked grain and pork country back of it." Despite its appearance of order and moral rectitude, a decency even the cats curled up in the sunshine on the houses' window-boxes seem to express, Dawson's Landing is fundamentally corrupt. Not only does the town have to be regarded as morally suspect, but anyone involved with it and with the main source of its corruption must be regarded as morally suspect too. This includes the Capello twins, who seem to choose to settle in Dawson's Landing almost at random.

losing side and had to fly for his life." Musical prodigies at age ten, orphaned and in debt, the twins were "placed among the attractions of a cheap museum in Berlin to earn the liquidation money. It took us two years to get out of that slavery." Following this, they took their show on the road, they claim, traveling the world only to retire to...Dawson's Landing. When the twins play, the townspeople are

Angelo and Luigi Capello

The Italians make their moral turpitude clear in the story of the murder. Angelo claims that his brother killed a thief in order to protect him; Luigi replies, "For unselfishness, or heroism, or magnanimity, the circumstances won't stand scrutiny. You overlook one detail: suppose I hadn't saved Angelo's life, what would have become of mine? If I had let the man kill him, wouldn't he have killed me too?" Whatever excuse he has for having murdered a man must be taken at half value in any case, given the explanation the Capello brothers give for their presence in Dawson's Landing. "We were of the old Florentine nobility," Angelo explains, "and when the war broke out my father was on the

"astonished and enchanted with the magnificence of their performance," but Twain describes it as merely "a prodigious slam banging." With their tales of exotic travel and noble roots, the Italian twins are most likely a couple of con-men in search of a gullible village to take, like the King and the Duke in Twain's *Adventures of Huckleberry Finn*. It's just as likely that they concocted the story of the murder of the Indian thief as that it really happened the way they said. As readers we must at very least withhold judgment. Their actions after the trial don't inspire confidence. They "were heroes of romance now, and with rehabilitated reputations. But they were weary of Western adventure, and straightway retired to Europe."

York Driscoll, Pembroke Howard, and the other FFVs

In order to claim leadership in Dawson's Landing, a man must trace his ancestry back to the First Families of Virginia, as do the Driscolls and Pem Howard. Howard, further, is "a gentleman according to the nicest requirements of the Virginian rule" and an authority on all matters connected to the

code of such a gentleman. That means he would take to the field of honor with the slightest provocation and duel "with any weapon you might prefer from brad-awls to artillery." When York Driscoll discovers that his nephew retaliated against Luigi for kicking him by taking him to court, "The old man shrank suddenly together like one who had received a death-stroke." According to Howard, this report, even though true, is "a cruel piece of slander." When Tom admits his mishandling of the affront to his honor, the Judge curses him, "You cur! You scum! You vermin! Do you mean to tell me that blood of my race has suffered a blow and crawled to a court of

law about it?" To Driscoll and Howard and all the FFVs, the court and the law apply only to the people, for whom they are perhaps useful protections. Superior men, as they believe themselves to be, have their code of honor to help them find justice. But these men, over sixty and risking their lives in resentment of a drubbing a relative deserved, appear only ridiculous and out of touch to us. Twain handles the duel itself with mock seriousness. Roxy reports the proceedings with due respect, but the duel itself is a comedy of errors. Luigi is struck three times, each one a glancing blow, and according to Roxy "we all got hit 'cep' de blon' twin en de doctor en de seconds. De Judge didn't git hurt, but I head Pudd'nhead say de bullet snip some o' his ha'r off." The duel itself is every bit as ridiculous as the FFV perception of classes of men.

Roxy

Without question, Mark Twain intends his readers to see Roxana as an heroic character. "She was of majestic form and stature," he writes; "her attitudes were imposing and statuesque, and her gestures and movements distinguished by a noble and stately grace." And it's Roxy, and Roxy alone, who dares to strike a blow against the empire, to challenge the "fiction of law and custom" that determined which human beings were free and which subject to the same treatment as cattle. Her effort fails, of course; that is the plot of the novel. Even in Greek tragedy, when heroes act counter to the laws of society, they fail. In *Oedipus*, a great hero murders his father and marries his mother (he doesn't know who his parents are) and great misery follows. Upon discovery of the truth, his mother Jocasta hangs herself and Oedipus blinds himself; only then is order restored. As Roxy finds her justice at the end of *Pudd'nhead Wilson*, "the spirit in her eye was quenched, her martial bearing departed with

it, and the voice of her laughter ceased in the land. In her church and its affairs she found her only solace." Society has reasserted itself, true, but it's an evil society. The legitimate Driscoll heir, having been cowed by his life of slavery, cannot rise to the position foisted upon him.

Perhaps Roxy is destined to fail because she herself accepts the unjust principles which guide Dawson's Landing. When she feels morally uncertain about having switched the babies, she recalls a biblical story along the same lines and so tells herself, "it ain't no sin, 'ca'se white folks done it. *Dey* done it—yes, *dey* done it; en not on'y jis' common white folks nuther, but de biggest quality dey is." She tries to soothe Tom's self-respect by telling him "Dey ain't another nigger in dis town dat's as high-bawn as you is," but when he fails to follow the gentleman's code and duel Luigi Capello, Roxy accuses him of succumbing to his black blood. "It's de nigger in you, dat's what it is. Thirty-one parts o' you is white, en on'y one part nigger, en dat po' little one part is yo' *soul*. Tain't wuth savin'; tain't wuth totin' out on a shovel en throwin' in de gutter." In her total acceptance of her world's corrupt ideology, she dooms her greatest dream to failure.

Pudd'nhead Wilson

Most modern readers are persuaded that Twain meant us to see Pudd'nhead Wilson as a hero, though a hugely nontraditional one. What does he do in the course of the novel that earns him the title of hero? He has the respect and friendship of York Driscoll, of course, but that is a tainted virtue: the friendship of powerful people is less impressive when the rules by which they live are suspect and the community they govern is corrupt. He befriends the Italian twins and stands by them even when the sentiment of the community has turned against them, but again, friendship with con-men is a dubious honor. In fact, before the trial, Wilson does very little to further the plot. He interests himself in the robberies plaguing Dawson's Landing and comes up with a clever plan by which to nab the thief, but then unwittingly reveals the plan to the thief—Tom Driscoll. He runs for mayor and wins, but on the strength of his association with the duel, in which "the people took more pride . . . than in all the other events put together." He hasn't enough power to carry his friends, the Capellos, into office and, besides, we all know the value of the office of mayor of a place as corrupt as Dawson's Landing.

THE CORONER'S JURY FOUND LUIGI GUILTY OF MURDER, AND HE AND HIS BROTHER WERE TO STAND TRIAL ONE DAY, WILSON VISITED THE TWINS.

IT'S NICE OF YOU TO COME. YOU AND MRS. COOPER ARE THE ONLY VISITORS WE HAVE.

Wilson's chief virtue isn't in action, and so he's not a hero in any traditional sense. He's a hero in wisdom. We are meant to credit him with Twain's pithy sayings, which head each of the chapters: "One of the most striking differences between a cat and a lie is that a cat has only nine lives." "Nothing so need reforming as other people's habits." And "It was wonderful to find America, but it would have been more wonder to miss it." Wilson's fellow freethinker, Judge Driscoll, likes these sayings and shares them with the townspeople, who regard them as sorry proof of Wilson's foolishness, like his finger-printing. As Twain remarks, "an enemy can partly ruin a man, but it takes a good-natured injudicious friend to complete the thing and make it perfect." And despite the indignities which Dawson's Landing visits on David Wilson, he stays. Peculiar though it is, it's his key virtue: He endures. Perhaps as an agent of wisdom and the standard-bearer of individualism, he can change Dawson's Landing.

•Much has been made of the invisible dog which barks so annoyingly when David Wilson first arrives in Dawson's Landing. Some people have seen it as the symbols of the town's stupidity, others of its injustice, still others of its racism. Some critics have seen David Wilson's final ascendance as his taking possession of "half that dog." What symbolic significance can you attach to the barking dog?

•Mark Twain builds *Pudd'nhead Wilson* on balancing pairs: the Italian twins, Tom and Chambers, Roxy and Wilson. How do these pairs balance one another? How many other pairs can you find in the novel? What is his point in using this symmetry?

•Race is one of the most troubling aspects of the novel. Even when Roxy appears to protest the unjust system of race slavery, she is in fact merely trying to preserve her own. No one in the novel answers her accusation that her son's small percentage of African blood makes him behave as badly as he does. What is Mark Twain's perspective on race, as represented by *Pudd'nhead Wilson* ?

•Throughout the novel, Mark Twain uses eye dialect—nonstandard spelling—to represent nonstandard language. Notice that he does not use this technique to represent the speech of Angelo and Luigi Capello, who presumably speak English with as strong an accent as do the slaves of Dawson's Landing. Why does he do this?

•In a century of use of finger-prints, we have learned that although these minuscule lines tell us everything we need to know to *identify* someone, they tell us nothing about that person's *identity*. In *Pudd'nhead Wilson*, Twain seems to fudge the distinction between identification and identity. What are the differences? How are each of these idea used in the novel?

•Clemens described his final revision of *Pudd'nhead Wilson* as economical. He wrote his publisher that he had "knocked out everything that delayed the march of the story—even the description of a Mississippi

AS SOON AS TOM LEFT...

I FEEL SORRY FOR HIM, EVEN THOUGH HE IS A MISERABLE DOG.

steamboat. There ain't any weather in it, and there ain't any scenery—the story is stripped for flight." Was Clemens too stingy with his story? Should he have included more detail? Of what sort? Why?

•At the end of the novel, Twain describes the attempted return of the true Thomas á Becket Driscoll—that is Chambers—to his position of community leadership, though he "could not endure the terrors of the white man's parlour, and felt at home and at peace nowhere but in the kitchen." Twain then refuses to follow his "curious fate" further, but some critics have noted that it would make a more interesting story than the one he had just concluded. Do you agree? How would you tell the story of Chambers's sudden elevation from slave to slave-holder?

•It's possible to read *Pudd'nhead Wilson* as a debate between two strategies of how to change an unjust society, through Roxy's radical, though perhaps self-destructive actions, or David Wilson's gentle, and perhaps ineffective, persuasion. When the injustice is as great as slavery, which avenue of social change do you advocate? How do you relate your choice to the fates of Twain's characters?

•Do you believe that people have an essential self, as David Wilson implies in his study of finger prints, or do you think people's actions are determined by their circumstances, as the remainder of the novel suggests? Use the novel to defend your point of view.

•Early in the novel, Percy Driscoll sells his thieving slaves locally instead of down river. This action is seen as generous, even magnanimous. Do you see it that way? Remember too that it's this turn of events which pro-vokes Roxy to switch the babies in her care. Can you justify her actions? Would you do the same thing if it were your child at risk, remembering that this child is the result of a liaison with anoth-er member of the elite of Dawson's landing? Why or why not?

About the Essayist:

Andrew Jay Hoffman is the author of *Inventing Mark Twain*: a biography of Samuel Langhorne Clemens; *Beehive*, a novel; and *Twain's Heroes, Twain's Worlds*. A visiting scholar at Brown University, he holds a Ph.D. in Literature from Brown.